Math K
An Incremental Development

Home Study Meeting Book

Name _____

Saxon Publishers, Inc.

Math K: An Incremental Development

Meeting Book

Printed in the United States of America

ISBN: 1-56577-021-8

Production Supervisor: David Pond
Graphic Artists: John Chitwood and Roger Hall

20 0982 18
4500699080

┌──── *Reaching us via the Internet* ────┐
www.saxonpublishers.com
E-mail: info@saxonpublishers.com
└──┘

Math K
An Incremental Development

Home Study
Meeting Book

Saxon Publishers, Inc.

September

Sunday	Monday	Tuesday	Wednesd

September

Thursday	Friday	Saturday

Sunday
Monday
Tuesday
Wednesday
Thursday
Friday
Saturday

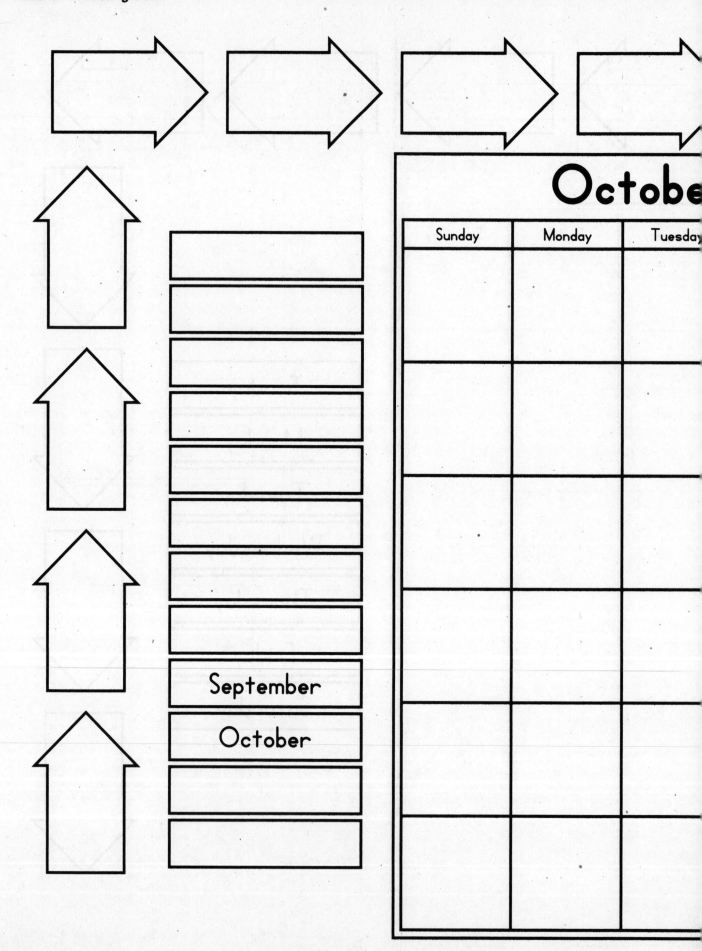

September

October

October

Sunday	Monday	Tuesday

...ednesday	Thursday	Friday	Saturday

Sunday

Monday

Tuesday

Wednesday

Thursday

Friday

Saturday

November

Sunday	Monday	Tuesday	Wednesday

September

October

November

hursday	Friday	Saturday

| Sunday |
| Monday |
| Tuesday |
| Wednesday |
| Thursday |
| Friday |
| Saturday |

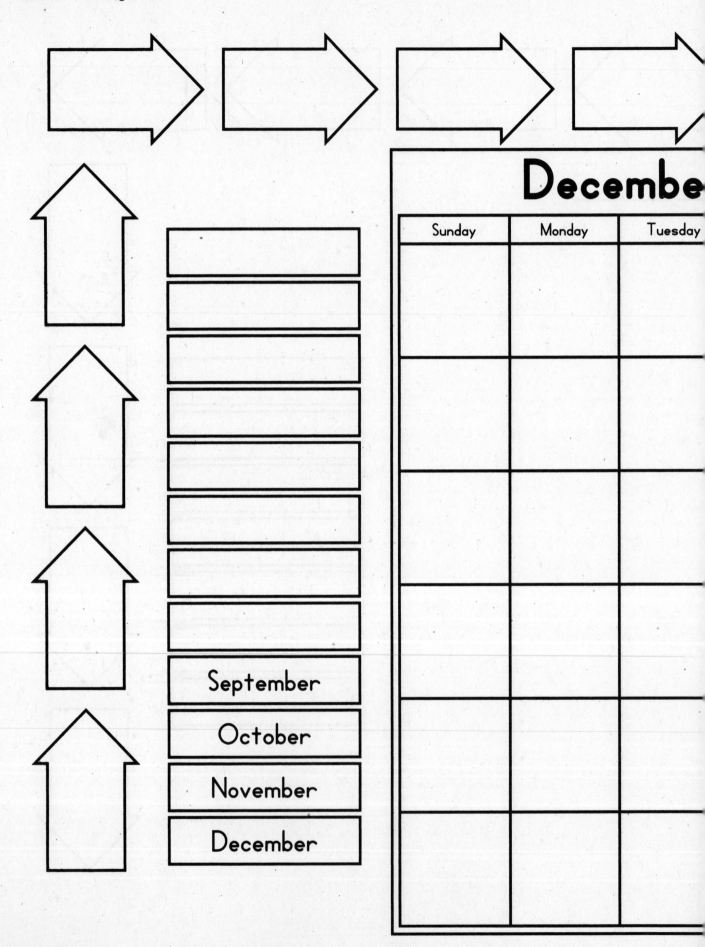

September

October

November

December

December

Sunday	Monday	Tuesday

ednesday	Thursday	Friday	Saturday

Sunday
Monday
Tuesday
Wednesday
Thursday
Friday
Saturday

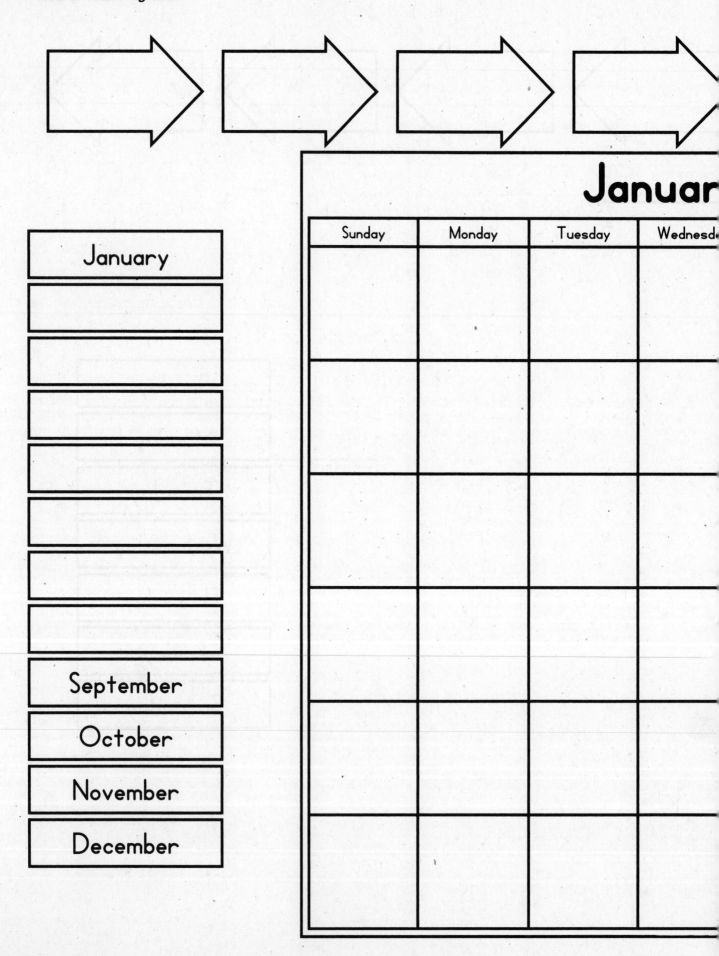

January

September

October

November

December

Januar

Sunday	Monday	Tuesday	Wednesd

Thursday	Friday	Saturday

Sunday
Monday
Tuesday
Wednesday
Thursday
Friday
Saturday

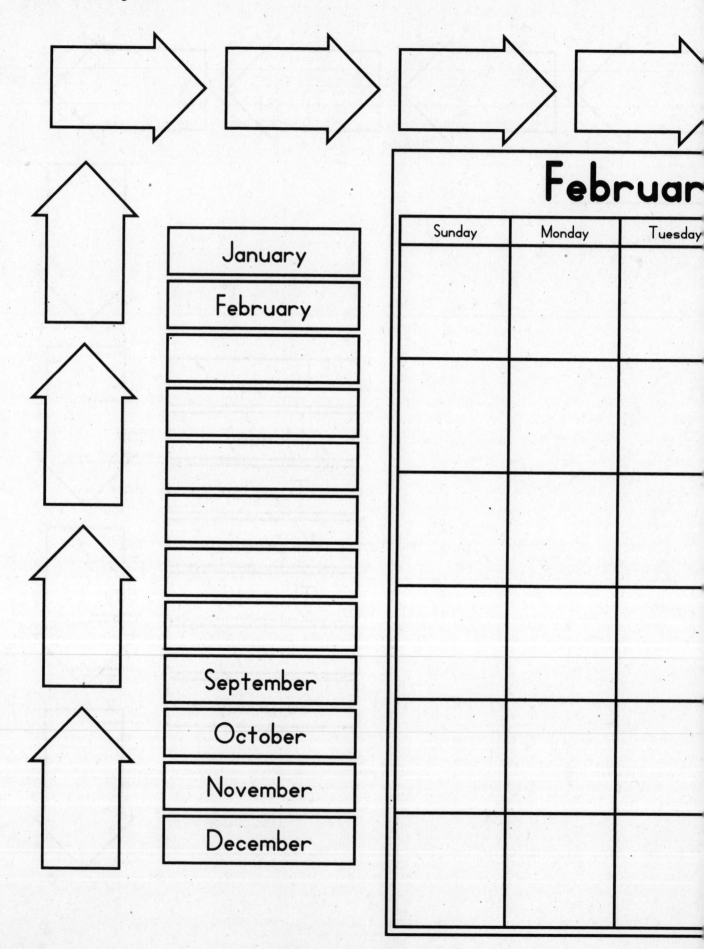

	February	
Sunday	Monday	Tuesday

January

February

September

October

November

December

Wednesday	Thursday	Friday	Saturday

Sunday
Monday
Tuesday
Wednesday
Thursday
Friday
Saturday

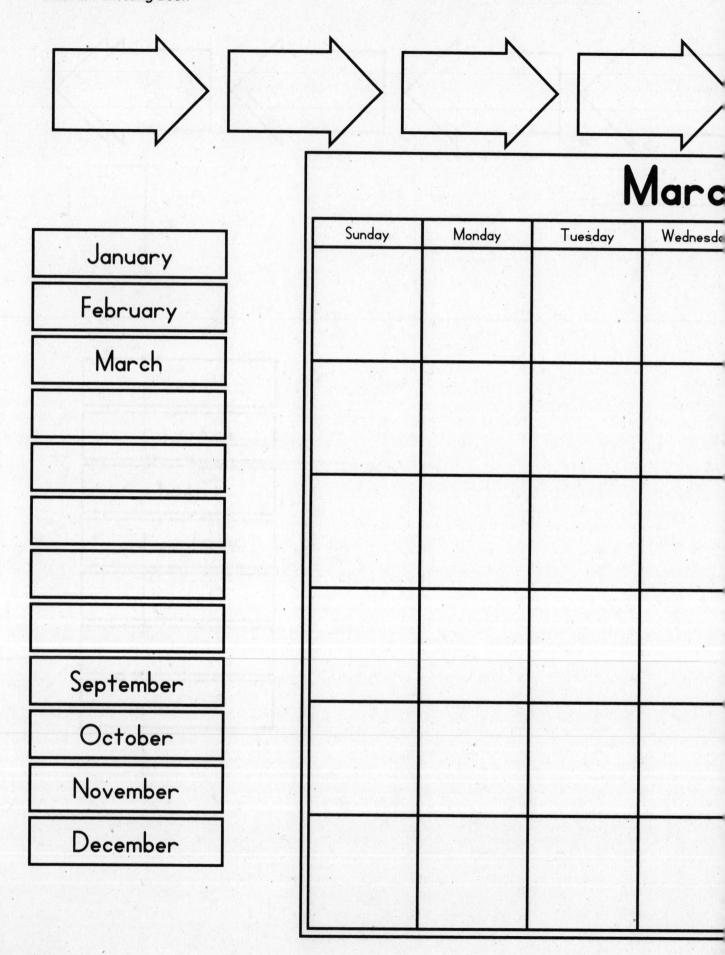

January			
February			
March			

	Sunday	Monday	Tuesday	Wednesda

Marc

January

February

March

September

October

November

December

Thursday	Friday	Saturday

Sunday

Monday

Tuesday

Wednesday

Thursday

Friday

Saturday

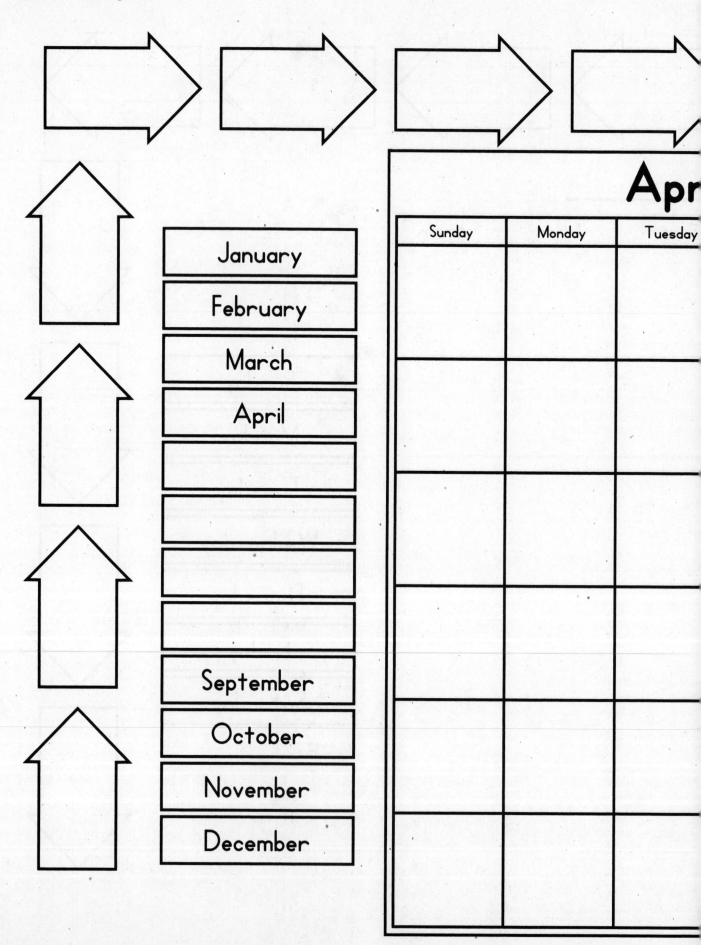

		Sunday	Monday	Tuesday

January

February

March

April

September

October

November

December

Apr

Wednesday	Thursday	Friday	Saturday

Sunday

Monday

Tuesday

Wednesday

Thursday

Friday

Saturday

Mo

Sunday	Monday	Tuesday	Wednesda

January
February
March
April
May
September
October
November
December

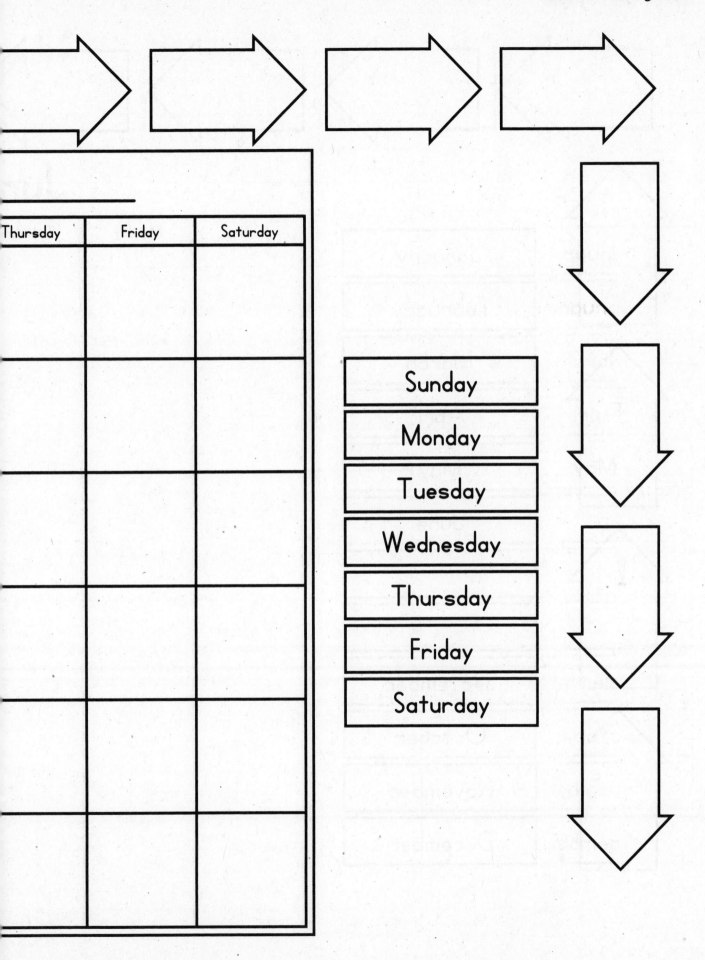

Thursday	Friday	Saturday

Sunday

Monday

Tuesday

Wednesday

Thursday

Friday

Saturday

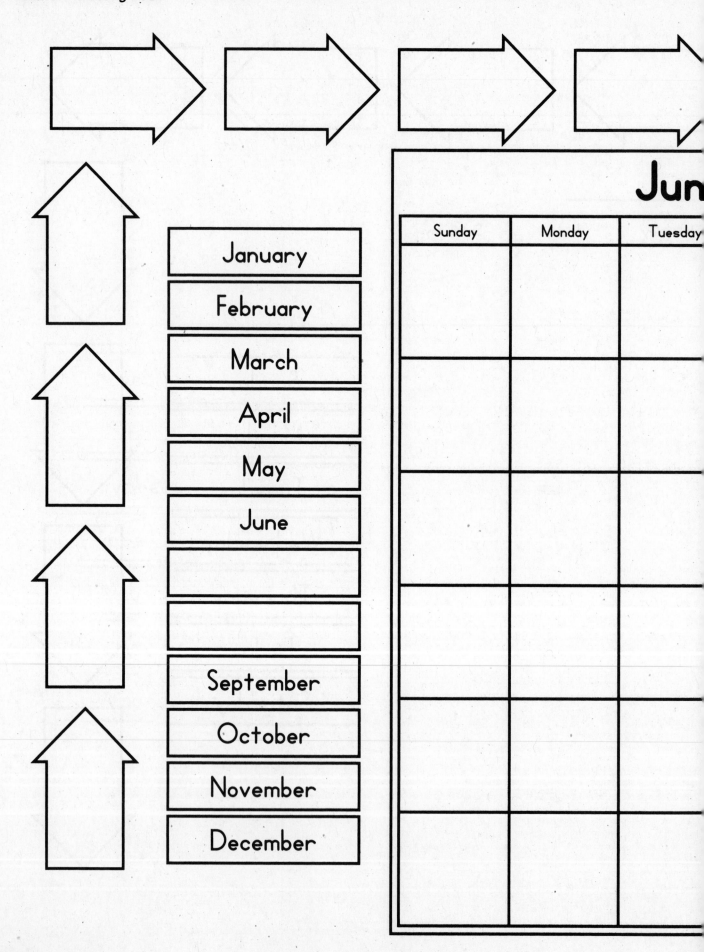

January

February

March

April

May

June

September

October

November

December

Jun

Sunday	Monday	Tuesday

Wednesday	Thursday	Friday	Saturday

Sunday

Monday

Tuesday

Wednesday

Thursday

Friday

Saturday

Pattern Block Shapes

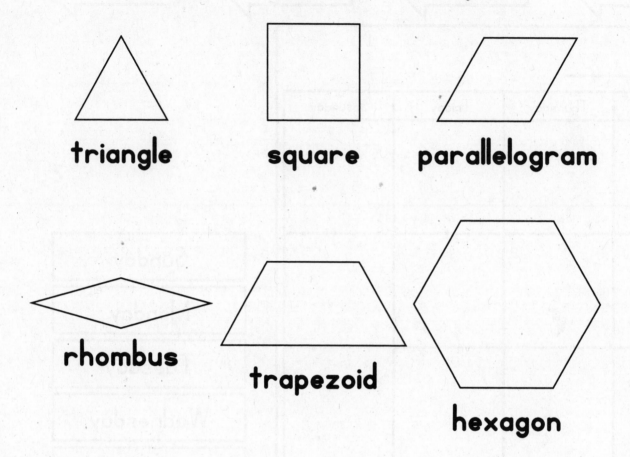

triangle   square   parallelogram

rhombus   trapezoid   hexagon

Color the triangle green.
Color the square orange.
Color the parallelogram blue.
Color the rhombus tan.
Color the trapezoid red.
Color the hexagon yellow.